ORPHEUS and EURIDICE

Opera in Four Acts

Music by

C. W. von Gluck

Libretto by
RANIERI DE CALZABIGI

English Translation by
WALTER DUCLOUX

D1502241

Ed. 2323

G. SCHIRMER
NEW YORK

NOTE

G. SCHIRMER, INC.
3 East 43rd Street
New York 17, N. Y.

PREFACE

For almost a century, Christoph Willibald Gluck (1714-1787) has been the earliest operatic composer represented in the repertory of opera houses of the world. A craftsman steeped in the traditions of his time, he matured slowly. His dramatic genius came to full fruition in his late forties, with *Orpheus and Euridice* soon to be followed by *Alcestis, Iphigenia in Aulis, Armida* and *Iphigenia on Tauris.*

History has come to recognize Gluck as the most important dramatic composer before Mozart. He has been proclaimed as a revolutionary who cleansed the mid-18th century musical theater of its weaknesses and brought about a sorely needed reform. In fact, Gluck shares this honor with a number of less well-known composers, librettists, choreographers and other creative artists bent on curbing the excesses of crusty formalism and interpretative license which had made the musical theater of their day a mockery of the ideals animating earlier operatic masters: a thorough integration of word and music, a subordination of all contributing elements to fundamental dramatic aims, a striving for dramatic substance of the highest ethical order expressed in the kind of exalted simplicity found in the ancient Greek tragedies.

Luckily, Gluck found a congenial and equally high-minded literary collaborator in the Italian diplomat-poet Ranieri da Calzabigi who wrote the text for several of Gluck's works, including *Orpheus* and *Alceste.* Their collaboration was no less noteworthy than that of later "teams" of Mozart and Da Ponte, Richard Strauss and Hofmannsthal. Unlike Mozart, Gluck was not a universal musician at home in any musical medium. To the core a man of the theater he, like Wagner, saw in the theater the supreme challenge to any composer. To him, to be "theatrical" meant to be truly artistic. This attitude, evident on every page of his music, has kept his masterworks alive through all the metamorphoses of style and public taste.

Orpheus, first performed in Vienna in 1762 in the original Italian was revised extensively for performance in Paris twelve years later. Not only was the vocal line changed to accommodate the French text, but the title-role, originally set for male contralto, was re-written for tenor. In addition, the Paris version contains several numbers not written for the Vienna version. The present edition is the result of a careful amalgamation of the two versions, leaving the title role to a contralto. The Appendix contains two portions of the original Vienna score, now usually omitted in performance.

Orpheus, like its composer, was slow in gaining the recognition it was eventually to achieve. Its very nobility and the stark simplicity of its texture, put it at a disadvantage compared to the lighter fare of comic opera and later the swashbuckling blood-and-thunder works of the romantic period. Yet, among all the works created for the musical stage, none more thoroughly achieves the ideal aim of theater as defined by the ancient Greeks: a *katharsis* or purification of the soul permitted to cleanse itself in the crystal waters of heavenly inspiration.

Walter Ducloux

CAST

ORPHEUS . . . . Contralto
EURIDICE . . . . Soprano
LOVE . . . . Soprano
A BLESSED SPIRIT . . . . Soprano

CHORUS . . . . {
   a. Shepherds and Shepherdesses
   b. Furies and Monsters
   c. Blessed Shadows

The action takes place in Greece, at an unspecified time in antiquity.

SYNOPSIS

ACT I A GROVE SURROUNDING EURIDICE'S GRAVE

A group of shepherds and shepherdesses are lamenting the death of Euridice. Orpheus, the celebrated singer and Euridice's bereaved husband, bids the others leave. After pouring out his grief, he appeals to the cruel gods of the Underworld, offering to descend to Hades to abduct his wife from the Realm of the Dead. Amor, the God of Love, informs Orpheus his request has been granted. He shall descend and bring back his wife provided he refrain from looking at her before their re-emergence on earth. Moreover, he is not to tell her of this condition. Orpheus, sensing the torment to which this decree will subject them both, accepts the challenge and proceeds to the Underworld.

ACT II AT THE GATES OF THE UNDERWORLD

The terrifying Monsters and Furies guarding the entrance to the Realm of the Dead at first refuse the wanton mortal. Gradually their wrath is soothed by the beauty of Orpheus' singing and he is admitted through the gate. Orpheus proceeds to the Elysian Fields, the domain of the Blessed Spirits.

THE ELYSIAN FIELDS

Orpheus is welcomed by a chorus of Blessed Spirits. Deeply moved by the beauty and peace around him, he soon remembers the purpose of his coming and asks the gods to guide him to Euridice. She is brought in by a group of Blessed Spirits. Orpheus, carefully averting his eyes, leads her on the way back to earth.

ACT III A SOMBER VAULT IN THE UNDERWORLD

Euridice has become aware of the identity of her rescuer, although she has not seen his face. She is dismayed by his refusal to look at her. Orpheus, unable to give an explanation for his strange behavior, urges her to follow him. Euridice starts doubting his love. When her anxiety turns to despair, Orpheus, no longer able to control himself, turns to her and dooms her forever. She dies. He attempts suicide but is stopped by the God of Love. Orpheus' devotion and loyalty have induced the gods to waive the fatal clause. Amor guides Orpheus and the reawakened Euridice back to earth.

NEAR THE TEMPLE OF LOVE

Happily reunited with their friends and companions, Orpheus and Euridice join in the praise of Love as the dominant force in the world to which everyone should pay a joyous tribute.

CONTENTS

ACT I

SCENE 1
Orpheus, Shepherds and Shepherdesses

SCENE 2
Orpheus

SCENE 3
The God of Love, Orpheus

SCENE 4
Orpheus

ACT II

SCENE 1
Orpheus, Chorus of Furies and Monsters

ORPHEUS AND EURIDICE

nglish translation by
Walter Ducloux

Overture

G. W. von **GLUCK**

Allegro molto

Act One

An attractive, secluded grove of laurel and cypress trees surrounding a clearing on which is seen the grave of Euridice. A group of shepherds and shepherdesses are decorating the grave with flowers; others throw incense on the sacrificial flame. Orpheus, slightly downstage from the group, is leaning against a rock and occasionally joins in the lament of the chorus.

La scène représente un bois de lauriers et de cyprès, un séjour agréable mais solitaire qui est entre-coupé pour former une petite plaine contenant le tombeau d'Euridice. — Au lever du rideau et pendant la ritournelle du chœur d'entrée, on voit une troupe de bergers et de nymphes dans la suite d'Orphée et tous portent des couronnes de fleurs et de myrtes; quelques-uns versent de l'encens dans le feu sacré, enguirlandent le marbre et couvrent son tombeau de fleurs, pendant que les autres chantent le chœur suivant qui est interrompu par les plaintes d'Orphée adossé sur le devant contre une pierre et répétant le nom d'Euridice d'une voix gémissante.

SCENE I

Orpheus. Shepherds and Shepherdesses

No. 1 Chorus

14

44522

No. 2 Recitative

Orpheus *Orphée*

Your sor-row and your grief In-crease my des-o-
Vos plain-tes, vos re-grets aug-men-tent mon sup-

la-tion. In fi-nal, de-vout in-vo-ca-tion Ap-
pli-ce! Aux ma-nes sa-cres d'Eu-ri-di-ce ren-

peal to her gods in your gloom, By strewing flow-ers on her tomb!
dez les su-prê-mes hon-neurs, et couvrez son tom-beau de fleurs.

No. 3 Pantomime

Lento

No. 4 Chorus

Lento

Soprano
Throughout this grove — all — joy has end-ed, Wings of dark-ness

Alto
Ah! dans ce bois lu-gubre et som-bre, Eu-ri-di-ce,

Tenor
Throughout this grove all joy has end-ed, Wings of dark-ness

Bass
Ah! dans ce bois lu-gubre et som-bre, Eu-ri-di-ce,

Lento

sotto voce

have de-scend-ed, Our Eu-ri-di-ce has died. — Hear our plead-ing,
si ton om-bre, si ton om-bre nous en-tend, sois — sen-si-ble

have de-scend-ed, Our Eu-ri-di-ce has died. — Hear our
si ton om-bre, si ton om-bre nous en-tend, sois sen-

si ton om-bre, si ton om-bre nous en-tend, Hear our plead-ing,
sois sen-si-ble a

cresc. *dim.* **F**

No. 5 Recitative

Orpheus *Orphée*

I bid you leave. A - lone my sor - row- strick - en
É - loi - gnez - vous; ce lieu con - vient à ma dou-

breast Shall once more sigh her name Where in death she will rest.
leur, et je veux sans té - moins y ré - pan - dre des pleurs.

No. 6 Ritornello

(The chorus exits.)-(Les bergers et les nymphes se dispersent dans le bois.)

SCENE II

Orpheus

No. 7 Aria

Now you, my love, have gone, Vain-ly I ask the dawn
Ob-jet de mon a - mour, je te de - mande au jour

Where to be near you, Where to be near
a - vant l'au - ro - re, a - vant l'au - ro -

you. For you my heart shall call
re; et quand le jour s'en fuit,

Long af - ter night must fall,— Hop-ing to hear — you, hop-ing to hear — you,
ma voix pen - dant la nuit— t'appelle en - co - re, t'ap-pelle en - co - re,

hop-ing to hear _____ you.
t'ap-pelle en - co - - - - - - re.

No. 8 Recitative

Orpheus *Orphée*

Dearest shad-ow, my be - lov - ed,
Eu - ri - di - ce, Eu - ri - di - ce,
My Eu - ri -di-ce, why no re -
om - bre chè - re, ah! dans quels

ply, no hope?
lieux es - tu?
Hear your husband, for - lorn, in dis -
Ton é - poux gé - mis - sant, in - ter -

may Cry-ing out to the dark - ness for - ev - er,
dit, é - per - du, te de - man - de sans ces - se,
Plead - ing in
à la na -

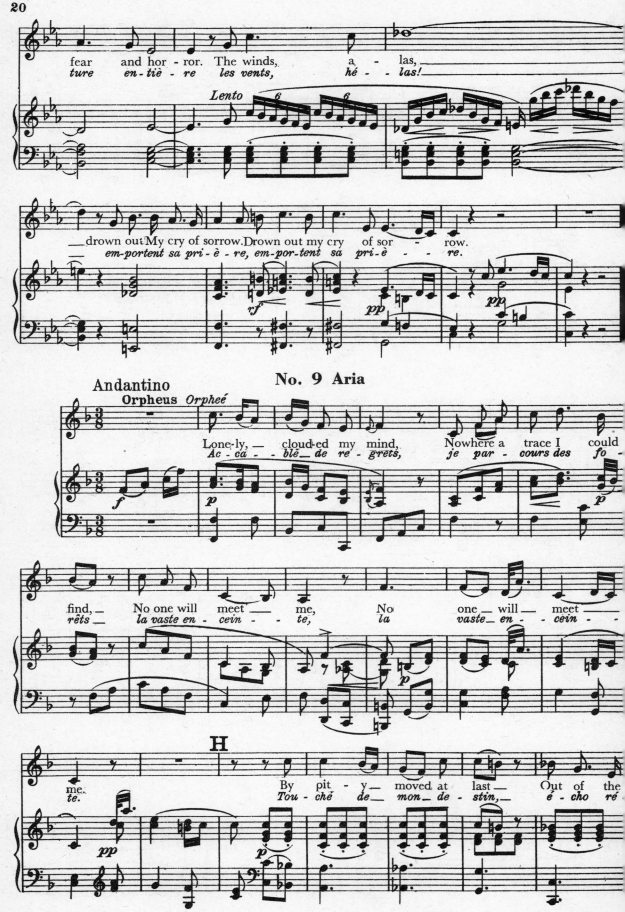

No. 9 Aria

Andantino

Orpheus *Orpheé*

Lone-ly,— cloud-ed my mind, Nowhere a trace I could
Ac - ca - blé de re - grets, je par - cours des fo -

find,— No one will meet me, No one will meet
rêts— la vaste en - cein - te, la vaste en - cein -

me.
te.

H

By pit-y moved at last— Out of the
Tou - ché de mon de - stin, é - cho ré -

No. 10 Recitative

Orpheus *Orphée*

hap-pi-ness and beau-ty. Eu-ri-di-ce has died, Death I myself pre-
u - ne main trem-blan-te. Eu-ri-di - ce n'est plus, et je respire en-

fer. Gods, give her back to me — Or let me die with her!
cor. Dieux, ren-dez - lui la vi - e, ou don-nez-moi la mort!

No. 11 Aria

Andantino
Orpheus *Orphée*

Filled with woe and de - spair, Rend-ing with sighs the
Plein de trouble et d'ef - froi, que de maux loin de

air, — My heart is sink - ing, My heart is sink -
toi, — mon cœur en - du - re, mon cœur en - du -

ing, The brook a - lone shall know How
re; té - moins de mes mal - heurs, sen -

free — my tears — can flow, — Tears it is drink - ing.
sible — à mes — dou - leurs, — l'on - de mur - mu - ré,

Tears it — is drink - - - ing, Tears it — is
l'on - de — mur - mu - - - ré, l'on - de mur -

drink - - - - - ing.
mu - - - - - ré.

No. 12 Recitative

Orpheus *Orphée*

You gods of A - che-ron's do - main, You grim and fear - some
Di - vi - ni - tés de l'A - ché - ron, mi - ni - stres re - dou -

lords Of the king-dom of dark - ness, You, whom down a - mong the shad - ows
tés de l'em - pi - re des om - bres, vous qui dans les de - meu - res som - bres

K

wife.
vir!

Without fear I descend To your re-gions in-fernal Where the
Je sau-rai pé-nétrer jusqu'au sombre ri-vage, mes ac-

pleas of my grief Will at last cool your ire. In your breast this hatred e-ter-nal Shall sub-
cents douloureux fléchi-ront vos rigueurs; je me sens as-sez de cou ra-ge pour bra-

SCENE III

The God of Love. Orpheus

Amor *L'Amour*

side before my pas-sion's fire! Your plea is not in vain. Your ap-
ver tou-tes vos fu-reurs. L'a-mour vient au se-cours de l'a-

peal has been heed-ed. The God of Love, I come here To grant you your quest. For to your
mant le plus ten-dre. Ras-su-re-toi, les dieux sont tou-chés de ton sort. Dans les en-

wish the gods have acceded: You shall find your belov-ed Where in death she must rest.
fers tu peux te rendre; va trou-ver Eu-ri-di-ce au sé-jour de la mort.
ten.

ten.

No. 13 Aria

L Amor *L'Amour*

Let your ten-der lyre's ——— sweet en-deav - or Fill with its
Si les doux ac - cords ——— de ta ly - re, si tes ac-

har - mo-ny the air. Its song ——— the sav-age fiends Shall be-calm in their
cents ——— mé - lo - di - eux ap - pai - - sent la fu - reur des ty-rans de ces

lair. ——— Yours she will be — once — more, Yours to be-hold for -
lieux, ——— tu la ra-mè - ne - ras du té-nébreux em-

ev - er. Yours she will be — once — more,
pi - re, tu la ra-mè - ne - - ras

Yours to be-hold for - ev - - - er.
du té - nébreux em - pi - - - re.

attacca

No. 14 Recitative

This is the gods' command And obey it you must To be wor-thy __ of their trust.
Tels sont de Ju-pi-ter les su-prêmes décrets. Rends-toi di-gne de ses bien-faits!

No. 15 Aria

Amor
L'Amour

Lento e grazioso

In
Sou -

si - lence to suf - fer, Your loved one so near, __ Is part of this of -
mis au si - len - ce, con-trains ton dé - sir, __ fais-toi vi - o - len -

fer. But soon will be end - ed Your tor - ment and fear. __ Yes, soon will be
ce, bien - tôt à ce prix tes tour - ments vont fi - nir, bien - tôt à ce

Meno lento

end - ed your tor - ment and fear.
prix tes tour - ments vont fi - nir.

To love in dis - tress __ Shows
Tu sais qu'un a - mant di -

44522

faith and de-vo-tion. Her ten-der ca - ress Will soothe your e - motion, You
scret et fi - dè - le, mu - et et trem - blant au - près de sa bel-le, en

soon will con - fess. Her faith and de - vo-tion Will soothe your e - mo-tion, For
est plus tou - chant; di - scret et fi - dè - le, au - près de sa bel - le

love is most no - ble In pain and dis - tress. Her faith and de - vo-tion Will
un a - mant en est plus tou - chant; au - près de sa belle un a -

Lento

soothe your e - mo - tion, You soon will con - fess. In
mant trem - blant en est plus tou - chant. Sou -

si - lence to suf-fer, Is part of this of - fer. But
mis au si - len - ce fais - toi vi - o - len - ce, bien -

32

Andante

Allegro

44522

faith be de-fend-ed! If Love should fail me now, My own life shall be end-ed!
maux que j'en-du-re. Dou-ter de ton bien-fait se-rait te faire in-ju-re.

Mighty gods, I pro-ceed, O-beying your command!
C'en est fait, dieux puissants, j'ac-cep-te vo-tre loi.

(See Appendix page 141)
(Voir Supplément page 141)

No. 17 Aria

Allegro maestoso

M
Orpheus *Orphée*

O' Love, I call you to
A - mour, viens rendre à mon

34

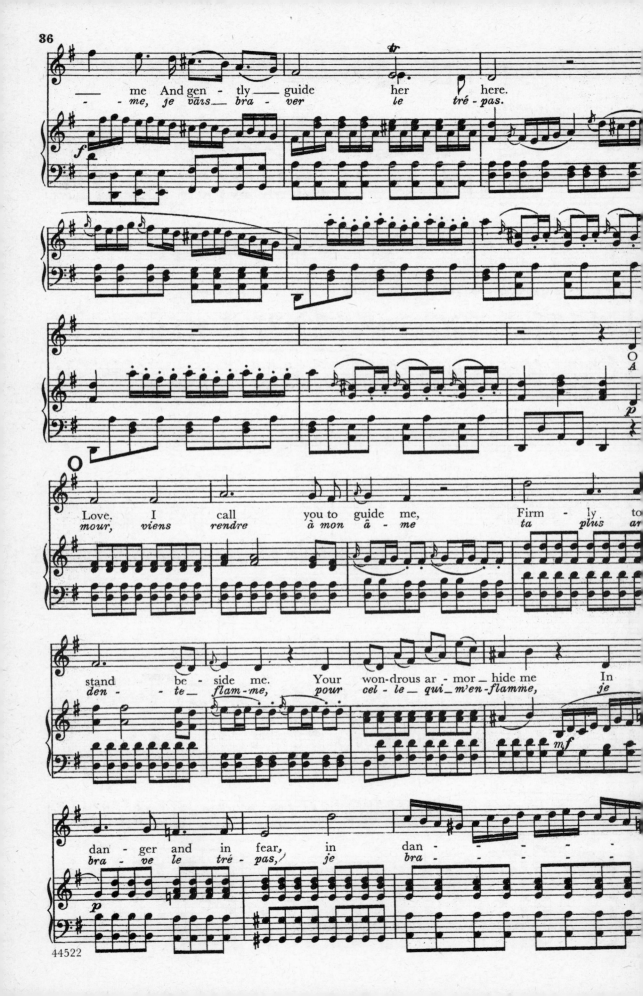

me And gen - tly guide her here.
- me, je vais bra - ver le tré - pas.

Love, I call you to guide me, Firm - ly to
mour, viens rendre à mon â - me ta plus ar

stand be - side me. Your won-drous ar - mor hide me In
den - te flam-me, pour cel - le qui m'en-flamme, je

dan - ger and in fear, in dan - - - - -
bra - ve le tré - pas, je bra - - - - -

me In ev-'ry dan-ger, ev-'ry fear! Now death shall hold her no
-me; je vais bra-ver— le tré-pas. L'en-fer en vain nous sé-

long-er, shall hold her no long-er.
pa-re, en vain nous sé-pa-re,

My heart will prove the strong-er, And ne
les mon-stres du tar-ta-re ne

Love will guide her here. Firm-ly walk-ing be
m'é-pou-van-tent pas. Je sens croî-tre ma

side flam-

me _ The God _ of.
- me, _ je vais bra-

Love will guide her here,
- ver le tré - pas,

The God of Love will guide her here.
je vais bra - ver le tré - pas.

End of Act I
Fin du premier acte

Act Two

A frightening, rocky landscape near the gates of the Underworld, veiled in a dark mist occasionally pierced by flames. The dance of the Furies and Monsters is interrupted by sounds of the lyre of the approaching ORPHEUS. When he comes into view they all join in the ensuing chorus.

Une contrée épouvantable, hérisée de rochers, au delà du Styx; au loin s'élève une fumée épaisse, sombre les flammes y jaillissent de temps en temps. Les spectres et les esprits commencent une danse qu' Orphée interrompt par l'harmonie de sa lyre; à la vue d'Orphée toute la troupe entonne le premier chœur qui suit

SCENE I

Orpheus. Furies and monsters of the underworld.

No. 18 Dance of the Furies

No. 19 Harp Solo Chorus

(Second orchestra backstage.)
2ᵈ orchestre derrière le théâtre.

44522

No. 20 Dance of the Furies

attacca

No. 21 Chorus

(The Furies dance around Orpheus to frighten him.)
(Pendant le chœur les esprits dansent autour d'Orphée pour l'effrayer.)

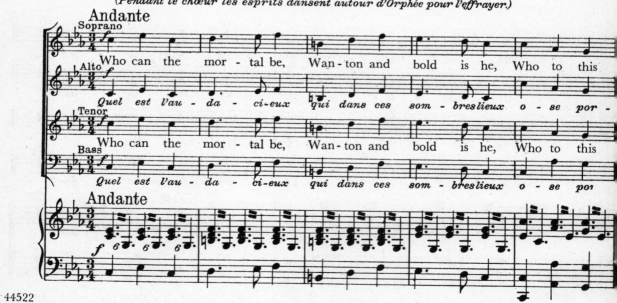

world of hate, Dar - ing a fright - 'ning fate, Has found the gate?

ter ses pas, et de - vant le tré - pas ne fré - mit pas?

world of hate, Dar - ing a fright - 'ning fate, Has found the gate?

ter ses pas, et de - vant le tré - pas ne fré - mit pas?

B

Ter - ror shall strike his heart, Tear - ing his mind a - part, When howl - ing

Que la peur, la ter - reur s'em - pa - rent de son cœur à l'af - freux

Ter - ror shall strike his heart, Tear - ing his mind a - part, When howl - ing

Que la peur, la ter - reur s'em - pa - rent de son cœur à l'af - freux

B

hell - hound's roar, Foam- drip - ping fangs a - jar, Bar him the door,

hur - - le - ment du Cer - bère é - - cumant et ru - gis - sant;

hell - hound's roar, Foam- drip - ping fangs a - jar, Bar him the door,

hur - - le - ment du Cer - bère é - - cumant et ru - gis - sant;

hell - hound's roar, Foam-drip-ping fangs a - jar, Bar him the

hur - - le-ment du Cer - bère é - - - cu-mant et ru - gis -

hell - hound's roar, Foam-drip-ping fangs a - jar, Bar him the

hur - - le-ment du Cer - bère é - - - cu-mant et ru - gis -

attacca

No. 22 Solo with Chorus

Un poco lento

Orpheus *Orphée*

Ah, have
Laïs-sez-

Soprano Alto
door.

Tenor
sant!

Bass
door.

Un poco lento

fp

pit - y, have pit - y on me!
vous tou - cher par mes pleurs,

Fu - ries!
spec - tres,

Mon-sters!
lar - ves,

No!
Non!

No!
non!

No!

No!

fp

p

fp

4522

No. 23 Chorus

(*The chorus answers Orpheus in a somewhat milder manner, showing signs of compassion*)
(*Le chœur apaisé répond à Orphée avec un peu plus de pitié dans l'expression.*)

Lyrics (English):

Having defied your fear Tell us who brought you here! Here is for life no room, Nothing but night and gloom, None but the cries of The damned in their doom. Having defied your fear Tell us who brought you here!

Lyrics (French):

Qui t'amène en ces lieux, mortel présomptueux? C'est le séjour affreux des remords dévorants et des gémissements et des tourments. Qui t'amène en ces lieux, mortel présomptueux?

Un poco lento · **Meno lento**

Soprano · Alto · Tenor · Bass

44522

No. 24 Aria

No. 25 Chorus

(In a milder manner) *(Encore plus apaisé.)*

Un poco lento

Soprano: Strangely the song he sings, Out of the night it brings, Balm to our

Alto: Par quels puis-sants ac-cords, dans le sé-jour des morts, mal-gré nos

Tenor: Strangely the song he sings, Out of the night it brings Balm to our

Bass: Par quels puis-sants ac-cords, dans le sé-jour des morts, mal-gré nos

fu-ry wild, Turn-ing our hearts be-guiled Peace-ful and mild.

vains ef-forts il cal-me la fu-reur de nos trans-ports?

fu-ry wild, Turn-ing our hearts be-guiled Peace-ful and mild.

vains ef-forts il cal-me la fu-reur de nos trans-ports?

Strangely the song he sings, Out of the night it brings Balm to our

Par quels puis-sants ac-cords, dans le sé-jour des morts, mal-gré tous

Strangely the song he sings, Out of the night it brings Balm to our

Par quels puis-sants ac-cords, dans le sé-jour des morts, mal-gré tous

44522

fu - ry wild, Turn-ing our hearts beguiled Peace - - ful and mild.

nos ef-forts, il cal - me la fu-reur de nos trans-ports?

fu - ry wild, Turn-ing our hearts beguiled Peace - - ful and mild.

nos ef-forts, il cal - me la fu-reur de nos trans-ports?

No. 26 Aria

Un poco lento   **Orpheus** *Orphée*

Here be - fore you I im - plore you, So your
La ten - dres-se qui me pres-se, cal - me-

wrath may soon a - bate. Tears shall tell you, and com-pel you To al-
ra vo - tre fu - reur, oui, mes lar-mes, mes a - lar-mes flé-chi-

low me through the gate. Tears shall tell you, and com-pel you To al-
ront vo-tre ri - gueur; mes a - lar-mes, mes lar-mes, fle-chi-

low me through the gate, To al - low me through the gate.
ront vo - tre ri - gueur, flé-chi - ront vo - tre ri - gueur.

No. 27 Chorus

(Almost completely subdued) (Encore plus doux.)

Andante

Soprano: Beau-ty un-known to us, Warm and me-lod-i-ous, Melt-ing our

Alto: *Quels chants doux et touchants, quels ac-cords ra-vis-sants! De si ten-*

Tenor: Beau-ty un-known to us, Warm and me-lod-i-ous, Melt-ing our

Bass: *Quels chants doux et touchants, quels ac-cords ra-vis-sants! De si ten-*

wrath a-way, Hold-ing our hearts in sway O-pen his way!

dres accents ont su nous dés-ar-mer et nous char-mer.

wrath a-way, Hold-ing our hearts in sway O-pen his way!

dres accents ont su nous dés-ar-mer et nous char-mer.

Allegro

So through the por-tals wide In may the mor-tal stride. He by the singer's art Conquered the

Qu'il descende aux en-fers! les che-mins sont ou-verts. Tout cède à la douceur de son art

So through the por-tals wide In may the mor-tal stride. He by the singer's art Conquered the

Qu'il descende aux en-fers! les che-mins sont ou-verts. Tout cède à la douceur de son art

Allegro

No. 28 Dance of the Furies

After the dance has started Orpheus enters the underworld. Towards the end of the dance, the Furies and monsters gradually disappear.

Après le commencement de cette danse, Orphée entre dans les enfers; vers la fin de la danse les spectres et les esprits disparaissent peu à peu.

44522

The Elysian Fields, domain of the Blessed Spirits. An enchanting landscape with bushes, flowers, brooklets, etc.

Une contrée enchanteresse des champs Elysées pleine de superbes buissons, de fleurs, de ruisseaux etc.

SCENE II

Chorus of the Blessed Spirits. Euridice.

Chœur des esprits bienheureux à l'Elysée; ensuite Euridice.

(The scene opens with a dance of the Blessed Spirits.)
(Le chœur ouvre la scène par une danse.)

No. 29 Ballet

No. 30 Ballet

No. 31 Ballet

Dolce, con espressione

Minore

Da Capo al Fine.

No. 32 Aria with Chorus

H

I

(*During the postlude Euridice and the Blessed Spirits slowly withdraw. Orpheus is lost in admiration.*)
Pendant le postlude disparaissent Euridice et les esprits bienheureux. Orphée est perdu dans l'admiration.

SCENE III
Orpheus

No. 33 Aria

Andante

p

With Pedal

speaks e-ter-nal peace.
é - ter-nel re - pos.

Yet, this en-chant-ment, This qui-et rap-ture Can-not end my de-spair and
Mais le cal - me qu'on y re-spi - re ne sau-rait a-dou-cir mes

grief.
maux.

For

you, on-ly you, My be-lov-ed my wife, Eu - ri - di-ce, can give me back my
toi, doux ob - jet de ma flam-me, toi seule y peux cal-mer le trou-ble de mon

O

life!
â - - me.

Once a-
Tes ac -

gain to lis - ten to her voice,
cents ten - dres et tou - chants,

P

In her smile to re - joice,
tes re - gards sé - dui - sants,

Once more to see her...
ton doux sou - ri - re

(Orpheus arouses the sympathy of the Blessed Spirts by his song and they return.)
(Attirés par le chant d'Orphée, les esprits bienheureux se sont rapprochés.)

Grant me, you gods, ———— this on-ly fa-vor!
sont les seuls biens ———— que je dé-si-re.

SCENE IV

Orpheus and Chorus of the Blessed Spirits

(Orpheus looks around as the Chorus approaches him.)
(Orphée regarde autour de lui, le chœur s'en approche.)

No. 34 Chorus

Soprano
Come, the Bless-ed Fields in-
Alto
Viens dans ce sé-jour pai-
Tenor
Come, the Bless-ed Fields in-
Bass
Viens dans ce sé-jour pai-

vite —— you, Hus-band ten-der, love shall de-light you, Come, and
si --ble, e-poux ten-dre, a-mant sen-si-ble, viens ban-
vite —— you, Hus-band ten-der, love shall de-light you, Come, and
si --ble, é-poux ten-dre, a-mant sen-si-ble, viens ban-

No. 35 Ballet

No. 36 Recitative and Chorus

Orpheus *Orphée*

But now, shadows that surround me, Do no longer withhold my loved one From my
O vous, ombres que j'im-plo-re, hâ-tez-vous de la rendre à mes embras-se-

arms! Ah, could you feel with me The torments that confound me, If you had known just
ments. Ah! si vous res-sen-tiez le feu qui me dé-vo-re, si vous é-tiez aus-

once A faith-ful lov-er's fire, I should be-hold her face Without all this de-
si de fi-dè-les a-mants, j'au-rais dé-jà re-vu la beauté que j'a-

lay.__ Lose no time, bring her back to me
do-re; hâ-tez-vous de me rendre heu-reux.

Soprano

So it be! Your wish be ful-filled!

Alto

Le de-stin ré-pond à tes voeux.

Tenor

So it be! Your wish be ful-filled!

Bass

Le de-stin ré-pond à tes voeux.

SCENE V
Euridice, Orpheus and Chorus of the Blessed Spirits

No. 37 Chorus

(Euridice is brought in by a group of the Spirits.)
(Euridice est introduite par une partie du choeur.)

plight - ed   To his faith - ful, lov - ing

sé - - e   au - près d'un si tendre é -

plight - ed   To his faith - ful, lov - ing

sé - - e   au - près d'un si tendre é -

wife.   To his faithful, faith - ful lov - ing wife.
au - près d'un si tendre, si tendre é - poux.

poux,   au - près d'un si tendre é - poux.

wife,   To his faith - ful, lov - ing wife.

poux,   au - près d'un si tendre é - poux.

(The Chorus leads Euridice to Orpheus. Without looking at her or being recognized by her, he tak
Euridice est ramenée à Orphée par le chœur; sans la regarder, il saisit sa main e

her hand and leads her away. The curtain falls slowly.)
l'emmène. — Le rideau se baisse lentement.

End of Act II
Fin du deuxième acte.

Act Three

A dark subterranean vault indicating a labyrinth of passageways amidst overhanging rocks covered with moss.
Une caverne sombre avec un labyrinthe plein de couloirs obscurs et entourée de rochers mousseux, tombants.

SCENE I
Orpheus, Euridice

(Orpheus still leads Euridice by the hand, without looking at her.)
(Orphée mème encore Euridice par la main sans la regarder.)

No. 38 Recitative

Orpheus Orphée

Oh come, Eu - ridice, oh
Viens, viens, Euridi-ce, suis-

Euridice

come! Once more to bliss-ful life, To my love you re - turn.__ 'Tis you? Can it
moi, u-nique et doux ob - jet de l'a-mour le plus tendre. C'est toi? je te

Orpheus Orphée

be? Gods, I can-not be-lieve it! _ Yes, you see your husband. My dis-
vois? ciel! de - vais - je m'at-ten-dre? Oui, tu vois ton é-poux. J'ai vou-

tress and my pain Gave me courage to tear you From Orcus a - gain. My pleas and bit-ter
lu vivre en-cor, et je viens t'ar-racher au sé-jour de la mort! Touché de mon ar-

Euridice

tears Have wak-ened in the gods Com-pas-sion and mer-cy. I, a
deur fi - dè - le, Ju - pi - ter au jour te rap - pel - le. Quoi! je

Orpheus
Orphée **A**

live and with you? Ah, great gods, what de-light! But, Eu - ri-di-ce,come with me! Let u
vis, et pour toi! Ah, grands dieux, quel bon-heur! Eu - ri - di - ce, suis-moi, pro-f

tar - ry no more, Blessed by our for - tune's fav - or! A - way at last from all this
tons sans re-tard de la fa-veur cé - le - ste; sor-tons, fuy-ons ce lieu fu

horror, From death and des-o - la - tion! Back to earth we as - cend 'Where all our sor-row sha
ne - ste. Non, tu n'es plus une om - bre, et le - dieu des a - mours va nous ré - u - nir pour tou

Euridice

end. But, tell me, how can this be? Such ec - sta-sy, such rap-ture! And so, once a
jours. Qu'entends-je? ah! se peut - il? heureu-se dé - sti - né - e! Eh quoi, nous po

pp

gain, you and I Shall be in hap-pi-ness u-nit-ed. Yes. Let us
rons res-ser-rer d'a-mour la chaî-ne for-tu-né-e? Oui, suis mes

B Euridice   Lento

flee with-out de-lay! Yet, now my hand Your own hand feels no long-er.
pas sans dif-fé-rer. Mais, par ta main ma main n'est plus pres-sé-e!

Why, a-vert-ing your eyes, You seem to flee my glance? Your heart,
Quoi! tu fuis ces re-gards que tu ché-ris-sais tant! Ton cœur

has it for-gotten How to beat ten-der and warm? Have I fad-ed in
pour Eu-ri-di-ce est-il in-dif-fé-rent? La fraîcheur de mes

Orpheus (*aside*)   (*Aloud*)
Orphée (à part).   (*haut*)

death, Lost my beau-ty and charm? O gods, how can I bear it? Let us leave here at
traits se-rait-elle ef-fa-cé-e? Oh dieux! quel-le con-trainte! Eu-ri-di-ce, suis-

Euridice

No, I stay. Death a-gain re-lieve me Of bit-ter de-cep-tion and pain!
Non, in-grat, *je préfère en-co-re la mort qui m'é-loi-gne de toi.*

grieve — me! See my
do - *re.* *Vois ma*

dolce

Leave me be - hind you!
Laisse Eu - ri - di - ce!

tor - ment! Ah, you wrong me. How could I find — you? U-
pei - ne! *Ah!* *cru - el - le! Quelle in-ju - sti - ce! Ah*

Tell — me your se - cret, I be-seech you! Oh
Par - le, *ré - ponds, — je t'en sup - pli - e;* *re*

nit - ed, we nev-er part' a - gain.
viens! je t'im-plo-re, suis mes pas!

poco a poco cresc.

tell — me, I be - seech you!
ponds, — je t'en sup - pli - e.

My se - cret I can-not teach you.
Dût - il m'encou-ter la vi - e,

p

90

Tempo I

44522

Più lento

No. 40 Recitative

Allegro moderato

round me fills the air.　　　　I am cold,　　　and I shake
tom - be sur mes yeux!　　　*Je fré - mis,*　　　*je lan - guis,*

as with fe - ver,　　　Am faint - ing,　　　feel - ing weak. . .
je fris - son - ne,　　　*je trem - ble,*　　　*je pâ - lis,*

My throb - bing heart　　beat - ing　wild - ly in fear　　and
mon cœur pal - pi - te, un　trou - ble se - cret　　m'a -

ter - ror,　　All my　sens - es are gripped　　with
gi - te,　　tous mes　sens　sont sai - sis　　d'hor -

fright!　Close in once　more, e - ter - nal night!
reur,　et je suc - combe à ma dou - leur.

No. 41 Aria and Duet

Duet — Duo
Andante

Orpheus *Orphée*

Andante

poco f

No. 42 Recitative

Orpheus *Orphée*

Gods, your com-mand is in-hu-man.
Quelle é-preu-ve cru-el-le!

Euridice

Ah, do not flee, be-lov-ed
Tu m'a-ban-don-nes, cher Or-

hus-band! Do not de-sert, in this hour of gloom And sor-row, the one who
phé-e! En ce mo-ment ton é-pou-se dé-so-lé-e im-plore en

needs you, Your wife. O gods, lend your help to my plea! Ere I shall end my
vain ton se-cours; ô Dieux! à vous seuls j'ai re-cours. Dois-je fi-nir mes

M   **Orpheus** *Orphée*

life, Grant me, my love, a fi-nal glance! My heart can no long-er re-
jours sans un re-gard de ce que j'ai-me? Je sens mon courage ex-pi-

sist. Slow-ly my mind turns mad, As in a hell-ish trance. My
rer, et ma rai-son se perd dans mon a-mour ex-trê-me; j'ou-

(He suddenly
turns to her.)
(Il se retourne
avec impétuosité

No, my wife shall not die,   For the   gods can-not will   it!   My Eu
Non, le ciel ne veut pas   un plus   grand sa-cri-fi-ce.   Oh ma

Euridice (*tries to rise, but sinks back again and dies*)
(*fait un effort de se lever, et meurt.*)

My Or-pheus.. fare-well . . .for-ev-er. . .
Or-phé-e! oh ciel! je meurs . . .

et regarde Euridice.)   Lento

ri-di-ce, be-lov-ed . . .   What, great gods, have I done! What a
chère Eu-ri-di-ce...   Mal-heureux,qu'ai-je fait?   et dans

Allegro

fright-ful dis-as-ter   Brought   on by my tor-tured love!
quel pré-ci-pi-ce   m'a plon-gé mon fu-neste a-mour?

See me weep-ing   here be-fore you,
Chère é-pou-se!   Eu-ri-di-ce!

cresc.

No. 43 Aria

Tempo I **P**

fright.   Now my love   has gone   for - ev - er.   All   my   days have turned to
cœur!   *J'ai per - du   mon Eu - ri - di - ce,   rien n'é - ga - le mon mal-*

night.   From my _ heart,_   gone for - ev - er   Ev -'ry   ray _ of _ hope and
heur;   sort_cru - el!_   quel-le ri - gueur,_ rien_n'é_ ga - le_ mon_ mal-

cresc.

light,   hope and light Have died for - ev - er   None_can_ know_my_ bit - ter
heur!   sort_cru - el!_   quel-le ri - gueur!_ je_ suc - combe_ à_ ma_ dou-

plight,   my _ bit - ter _ plight, _____   my _ bit - ter_ plight.
leur,   à_ ma_dou - leur, _____   à_ ma_dou - leur!

Orpheus *Orphée*

My o - verwhelming grief Shall find its grim con - clusion. I nev-er can sur-
Ah! puis - se ma dou - leur fi - nir a - vec ma vi - e! Je ne sur-vi-vrai

vive, A fate too harsh to bear. So once a - gain I shall de-scend to
point à ce der - nier re - vers. Je touche en - cor aux por-tes des en-

Ha-des And soon shall be with her, Eu - ri - di - ce, my wife.
fers, j'au-rai bien-tôt re - joint mon é - pou - se ché - ri - e.

Adagio

Yes, I shall fol - low you, my love, To the
Oui, je te suis, tendre ob - jet de ma

grave, stay with you for - ev - er, for - ev - er.
foi, je te suis, at - tends-moi, at - tends - moi!

No one shall ev - er take you from me Af - ter death does u -
Tu ne me se - ras plus ra - vi - e, et la mort pour ja -

SCENE II
The God of Love. Orpheus and Euridice.

Orpheus *Orphée*   **Euridice**   **Orpheus** *Orphée*

ward! My Eu-ri-di-ce! My Or-pheus! Al-might-y gods, Our grat-i-tude shall be un-
feux. Mon Eu-ri-di-ce! Or-phé-e! Ah! ju-stes dieux! quelle est no-tre re-con-nais-

Amor *L'Amour*

bounded. Your fears and doubts you find unfounded. But now without de-lay To brighter spheres a-
san-ce! Ne dou-tez plus de ma puis-san-ce! Je viens vous re-ti-rer de cet af-freux sé-

bove, To en-joy, as you may, The de-lights of your love!
jour, jou-is-sez dé-sor-mais des plai-sirs de l'a-mour!

SCENE III

The magnificent Temple of Love. The God of Love, Orpheus and Euridice enter preceded by a large group of shepherds and shepherdesses. The return of Euridice is celebrated by joyous songs and dances.

Un magnifique temple consacré à l'amour.—L'Amour, Orphée, Euridice. Devant eux marche une nombreuse troupe de bergers et de bergères fêtant le retour d'Euridice par leur chant et leurs joyeuses danses.

No. 45 Chorus and Soloists

Allegro leggiero

deav-or, Rule for - ev - er __ beaut-y's do - main! His chains will un-

spi - re sert l'em - pi - re __ de la beau - té; sa chaine a - gré-

deav-or, Rule for - ev - er beaut-y's do - main! His chains will un-

spi - re sert l'em - pi - re de la beau - té; sa chaine a - gré-

ite __ us, Charm, and de - light __ us. Slaves, we are hap-py in his

a - ble est pré - fé - ra - ble, est pré - fé - ra - ble à la

ite us, Charm, and de - light us.

a - ble est pré - fé - ra - ble,

bless - ed __ reign. Slaves, we are hap-py in his bless - ed __ reign.

li - ber - té, est pré - fé - ra - ble à la li - ber - té.

Slaves, we are hap-py in his bless - ed reign.

est pré - fé - ra - ble à la li - ber - té.

C Amor *L'Amour*

Pained, in an-guish, in doubt and sor - row,— Man-y a heart knows
Dans les pei - nes, dans les a - lar - mes— je fais sou - vent lan-

rain and storm. Yet, the sun will shine to- mor-row,
guir les cœurs; mais dans un in - stant mes char - mes

Lov - ing and heal - ing, so ten - der and warm, Lov - ing and heal - ing, so
font pour ja - mais ou - bli- er mes ri - gueurs, font pour ja - mais ou - bli-

ten - der and warm.
er mes ri - gueurs.

D

Let love tri-

L'a - mour tri-

Let love tri-

L'a - mour tri-

E Euridice

Jeal-ous and wild, my heart may suf-fer, Ten-der thoughts may flee my breast;
Si la cru - el - le ja - lou - si - e a trou - blé mes ten - dres dé - sirs,

Yet true love will have to of-fer Heal-ing balm and
les dou - ceurs dont elle est sui - vi - e, sont des chai - nes

sweet - est rest, Heal-ing balm and sweet-est rest.
de plai - sirs, sont des chaî - nes de plai - sirs.

F

Let love tri - um-phant Be guide in all en
L'a - mour tri - om - phe et tout ce qui re-

Let love tri - um-phant Be guide in all en
L'a - mour tri - om - phe et tout ce qui re-

F

deav-or, Rule for - ev - er— beaut-y's do - main! His chains will un-

spi - re sert l'em - pi - re— de la beau - té; sa chaine a - gre-

deav-or, Rule for - ev - er beaut-y's do - main! His chains will un-

spi - re sert l'em - pi - re de la beau - té; sa chaine a - gré-

ite — us, Charm, and de - light — us. Slaves, we are hap-py in his

a - ble est pré - fé - ra - ble, est pré - fé - ra - ble à la

ite us, Charm, and de - light us.

a - ble est pré - fé - ra - ble,

bless - ed — reign. Slaves, we are hap-py in his bless - ed— reign. Let

li - ber - té, est pré - fé - ra - ble à la li - ber - té. L'a-

Slaves, we are hap-py in his bless - ed reign. Let

est pré - fé - ra - ble à la li - ber - té. L'a-

G Allegro

G Allegro

No. 46 Ballet

No. 47 Gavotte

Dal Segno al Fine.

No. 48 Ballet

No. 49 Minuet

124

14522

No. 50 Trio

128

44522

No. 51 Ballet

No. 52 Ballet

W

No. 53 Chaconne

End of Opera
Fin de l'opéra.

Appendix

No. 1 Postlude to Recitative No. 16

If Aria No. 17 (allegedly by Bertoni) is to be cut.

(See page 33, Measure 6)

Supplément.

I. Postlude au récitatif Nº 16,

si l'air Nº 17 (attribué à Bertoni)
doit être supprimé.
(Voir page 33 mesure 6.)

(Thunder and lightning. Orpheus leaves quickly.)
(Eclair et tonnerre, Orphée s'enfuit.)

horchen!
lói.

Presto

II. Ballet

End of Act I
Fin du premier acte.

Allegro

142

Fine.

Dal Segno al Fine.

44522

G. SCHIRMER'S
CLOTH BOUND VOCAL SCORES OF
STANDARD OPERAS

BEETHOVEN.	Fidelio (*German and English*)	5.00
BELLINI.	La Sonnambula (*Italian and English*)	4.00
BELLINI.	Norma (*Italian*)	5.00
BIZET.	Carmen (*French and English*)	5.00
CHARPENTIER.	Louise (*French and English*)	7.50
DONIZETTI.	Lucia di Lammermoor (*Italian and English*)	4.00
FLOTOW.	Martha (*German and English*)	5.00
GLUCK	Orpheus and Euridice (*French and English*)	4.50
GOUNOD.	Faust (*French and English*)	5.00
GOUNOD.	Roméo et Juliette (*French and English*)	5.00
HERBERT.	Natoma (*English*)	5.00
HUMPERDINCK.	Hansel and Gretel (*English*)	4.00
LEONCAVALLO.	Pagliacci (*Italian and English*)	5.00
MASCAGNI.	Cavalleria Rusticana (*Italian and English*).	4.00
MASSENET.	Manon (*French and English*)	5.00
MOZART.	Così fan Tutte (*Italian and English*)	6.00
MOZART.	Don Giovanni (*Italian and English*)	5.00
MOZART.	Le Nozze di Figaro (*Italian and English*)	6.00
MOZART.	Die Zauberflöte (*German and English*)	5.00
NICOLAI.	The Merry Wives of Windsor. (*English*).................	5.00
OFFENBACH.	Les Contes d'Hoffmann (*French and English*)	6.00
PONCHIELLI.	La Gioconda (*Italian*)	5.00
PUCCINI.	La Bohème (*Italian and English*)	6.00
PUCCINI.	Tosca (*Italian and English*)	6.00
ROSSINI.	Il Barbiere di Siviglia (*Italian and English*)	5.00
SAINT-SAËNS.	Samson et Dalila (*French and English*)	5.00
SMETANA.	The Bartered Bride (*English*)	5.00
TCHAIKOVSKY.	Eugene Onégin (*German and English*)...................	5.00
TCHAIKOVSKY.	The Queen of Spades (Pique-Dame) (*English*)	5.00
THOMAS.	Mignon (*French and English*)	5.00
VERDI.	Aida (*Italian and English*).............................	5.00
VERDI.	Un Ballo in Maschera (*Italian and English*)	5.00
VERDI.	Rigoletto (*Italian and English*)	4.00
VERDI.	La Traviata (*Italian and English*)	4.00
VERDI.	Il Trovatore (*Italian and English*)	4.00
VERDI.	Otello (*Italian and English*).	6.00
WAGNER.	Der Fliegende Holländer (*German and English*)	4.00
WAGNER.	Götterdämmerung (*German and English*).................	7.50
WAGNER.	Lohengrin (*German and English*)	5.00
WAGNER.	Die Meistersinger von Nürnberg (*German and English*)	10.00
WAGNER.	Parsifal (*German and English*)	5.00
WAGNER.	Das Rheingold (*German and English*)	5.00
WAGNER.	Siegfried (*German and English*)	5.00
WAGNER.	Tannhäuser (*German and English*)	5.00
WAGNER.	Tristan und Isolde (*German and English*)	5.00
WAGNER.	Die Walküre (*German and English*)	5.00
WEBER.	Der Freischütz (*German and English*)....................	5.00

Prices subject to change without notice